ƭ 2·00ɔ

DATE

Agricultu

Occasiona

C000007969

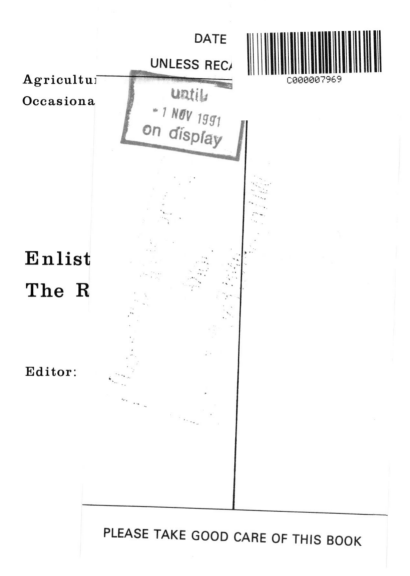

Enlist

The R

Editor:

Overseas Development Institute
10-11 Percy Street, London W1P 0JB
Telephone 01-580 7683

Overseas

Development

Institute

The Overseas Development Institute (ODI) is an independent, non-government body aiming to promote wise action in the field of overseas development. It was set up in 1960 and is financed by official grants and private donations from British and international sources. Its policies are determined by its Council.

The functions of the Institute are:
1 to be a centre for research on development problems and policies;
2 to stimulate and encourage discussion of development issues;
3 to keep the importance of development questions before the public and responsible authorities.

Agricultural

Administration

Unit

The Agricultural Administration Unit (AAU) was established
at ODI at the beginning of September 1975, with financial
support from the Ministry of Overseas Development (ODM).

As its title implies, the Unit is concerned with the
study of agricultural administration and institutions in
less developed countries, with the emphasis on field
implementation - the planning and programming of development, the provision and co-ordination of services, and
the support of participatory and self-managing groups.

It aims to widen the state of knowledge of agricultural
administration through a programme of policy-oriented
research into selected subject areas, the promotion of
informed debate, and the exchange of ideas and experience.
The Unit also seeks to influence directly the organisation
and management of agricultural development through the
provision of specialist advice. The scope of the AAU's
work is therefore threefold: research, dissemination and
advice.

A major objective of the AAU is to provide a bridge
between 'thinkers' and 'doers'. Accordingly, each research
subject is studied in collaboration with a 'network' of
individuals in the UK and overseas who have been directly
concerned with the problems of implementation in developing
countries. Network members are drawn from a wide range
of nationalities, professional backgrounds, and disciplines.
The Unit aims to keep itself well-informed on other
important aspects of the organisation and management of
agricultural development outside its specialist fields
and to help, to the extent it can, other organisations
and individuals engaged in related work.

The purpose of the AAU's 'Occasional Papers', is
to disseminate the findings of this collaborative effort
to a wide audience of interested people in an easily
accessible format. The first Paper, *Stimulating Local
Development*, appeared in 1976, the second, *Extension,
Planning, and the Poor*, in 1976, and the third, *Institutions,
Management, and Agricultural Development*, in 1979. All
three are available from ODI; numbers 1 and 2 at £1.00
each and number 3 at £2.00 per copy.

Further information about the work of the Unit may
be obtained from the AAU, Overseas Development Institute,
10-11 Percy Street, London W1P OJB.

Contents

INTRODUCTION

This paper springs from Discussion Paper No 6 in the ODI
Agricultural Administration Unit Network series, which
was entitled 'A Hard Look at Directing Benefits to the
Poor and at Participation'. Comments on that paper were
requested, and more than 20 considered comments were
received, some raising new issues, some amending or ques-
tioning the existing text. This new Occasional Paper is
aimed to share these comments with Network members, but
in a form which will also be intelligible to new readers.

Discussion Paper No 6 was structured by listing and
discussing a rather numerous list of assumptions which
it would be necessary to make if development programmes
more directly aimed at small and marginal farmers were
to meet the difficulties and objections which have been
raised against them, and which partly account for the
neglect of the very large section of the rural economy -
the poor.

This Occasional Paper takes a rather more positive
line. It is structured by listing and considering what
modifications would have to be made to commonly existing
policies, structures, attitudes and administrative arrangements if development of the poorer rural sections is to
be achieved on any considerable scale.[1] It does, therefore,
assume that change is desirable, and the emphasis is on
its nature and on its practicability.

---

1 'Enlisting the Small Farmer' implies winning his active
   participation in programmes on which he has been consulted, and which help to bring him a far greater share
   of development benefits.

The justification for change

The need for change can be justified in three main ways.
First, there is a moral argument against the injustice
and inequity of continued existence of dire poverty, in
all its deplorable aspects, in the present world; if it
can be remedied, to whatever extent, it should be. This
view may not be equally held everywhere; but there are
substantial signs, worldwide, that it does have an effect
at least on declared policies and to some extent in
action.

Second, there is an economic argument. It is hard
to deny that a great waste of human energy and intelli-
gence and of many physical resources (land, water) is
involved in the very existence of many millions of small
and marginal farmers at levels of productivity and of
consumption so far below both human and resource potential.
The changes which it has been possible to make where real
attention and effort has been devoted to this situation -
still, alas, in too few instances - are evidence that
much could be done. That there are costs to this effort
- particularly initial costs in personnel and training -
is not to be denied; but they must be weighed against the
costs of doing nothing.

Third, there is a political argument. The stability
of governments in countries where such a mass of poverty
continues, is always in question, and more questioned as
modern communication reveals ever more sharply the contrasts
and inequalities of the modern world.

The major obstacles to change

Out of a host of details, five major obstacles to changes
in the policies and practices of governments towards small
farmers and the rural poor stand out.

a) *The direct economic costs* in personnel, training, and
multiple minor investments, of servicing initially a large
new section of rural society - 'initially' because later
it should become far more self-supporting; 'new' because
very little *special* service has been given in the past
to this section.

b) *The political aspects of this cost* Here must be
mentioned a major comment by *Carey Jones*,[1] too long for
full quotation. His argument, in brief, runs as follows
(in my words). Any government depends for its survival
on its supporters - even if it uses guns, it depends on
those who carry them. From inevitably limited resources,
it must see to it that supporters receive a good slice
of benefits; and it can hope that by support of influential
followers, the mass of people behind them will be influenced
too. If resources are static, diverting a greater share
to the poor means giving less to wealthier or influential
supporters. Only if resources are growing substantially
can a larger constituency enter the area of benefit.
Governments will therefore look for the most profitable
investments and to the agents who are most likely to
manage them effectively and to generate a return on
investments, probably including foreign exchange. The
poor are not likely to be these agents; in fact what they
are likely to get is more in the nature of 'charity' or
sops to cool off unrest.

This comment, even if not acceptable, is important
because it represents an attitude - if not so frankly
expressed - which has had great influence. It is reflected
in the idea of 'backing winners'; it is reflected in one
aspect of the World Bank's policies - to finance projects
in the areas of best potential, of most progressive farmers,

---

1 A list of commentators is included in the Appendix.

with a high prospective rate of return; and it is reflected
in much macro-economic planning by governments in
developing countries. Two comments are in order here.
First, it is not self-evident that the poor are not
profitable and earn no foreign exchange. In commodity
schemes in particular (tea, coffee, palm products, and
many more) foreign exchange on a huge scale has been
earned by the product of very small holders and indeed
by groups often called 'primitive'. Second, it assumes
collective agreement by governments, as single, rational
decision-makers on a single strategy; and this in practice
does not seem to reflect the rivalries, jealousies and
often individualism of many of them. Further, the whole
argument does not do justice to the efforts now being
made by quite a number of governments, within their
limited resources, to devise new methods of bringing
greater development benefits to the poor.

c) *The socio-political pattern*   The first two obstacles
concern the hesitations of governments to face the economic
costs of expanding existing services, and perhaps adding
new ones, in order to include a very large and previously
neglected section of the rural population – and the fears
of governments that such a policy might alienate powerful
elements of political support. The other two obstacles
are of a rather different nature. *Assuming* that at least
some governments, despite these hesitations or fears, do
make an effort to reach the smaller and marginal farmers,
two very serious obstacles still stand in their way.
First, there is in most developing countries – as there
was in developed countries now endeavouring to sustain
a welfare state – a socio-political hierarchy, running
down through society, in which the richer, better educated
and more influential elements are able to appropriate to
themselves an unduly large share of the benefits of
economic development, allowing to the poor only that

meagre share which would bind some of them as dependent
clients and political supporters. The relationship of
dominance and dependency is pervasive. It is not
necessary for the dominants to have formal powers as
landlords or officials; their financial resources, their
commercial competence, their ability to handle officials,
to use the courts of law or the influence of a creditor
is enough to maintain their superior position, to become
chairman of a local council or co-operative, to obtain
quicker and better service from junior field staff.

d) *The special position of the poor* This is partly the
obverse of the power of the rich; but it would exist and
present difficulties of approach even if the rich did
not capture development benefits intended for all. The
very lack of assets, the rational fear of financial
risks, difficulties in dealing with officials, lack of
self-confidence of the poor, make special adaptation of
services to them necessary - and also difficult.

e) *The administration of change* This is a major difficulty of many facets, and showing itself in many different
contexts. It shows in the unwillingness to decentralise
(mainly by delegation) operational control and finance;
in the choice of institutions which governments elect
to favour; in the formulation of technical agricultural
programmes; and pervasively in the style and attitudes
of official bureaucratic management which run right down
to services at village level. The fact is that a decision
to include, in policy and programmes, a whole and very
large new element in rural society cannot be achieved
simply by adding to the existing administrative structure
some 'special' arrangements for 'the poor'. Such an
effort involves changes in extension, in research, in
institutional policy, in local planning and in the content
and objectives of the training and management of field
staff.

It should perhaps be emphasised that these major difficulties do not apply with the same force to all types of agricultural development. They apply with full force only if a viable system is to be created which will in fact meet the special needs of small and marginal farmers; which will give them some effective voice in the design of programmes for their benefit; and which will help them to participate actively in the management of such programmes. In consequence, this Occasional Paper will not deal with, for example, plantation systems or with special commodity schemes, in which the whole sequence of research, extension, credit and supply of inputs, processing and marketing is executed by a single crop authority or parastatal board or private company. It is concerned with the general country-wide approach to the small-holder growing a variety of crops and/or animals in which he himself makes the final decision of what to grow and how to grow it, in relation to his needs and to local physical and market conditions. It applies mainly to programmes and very little to those projects which are so heavily loaded with special staffing and finance that they cannot be widely applied.

The remainder of this Occasional Paper will deal with these obstacles and with the wide range of adjustments and changes which are required if programmes for this poorer section of the rural economy are to be genuinely successful.

PART I: CENTRAL ECONOMIC AND POLITICAL POLICIES

DIRECT ECONOMIC COSTS

That there will be extra recurrent costs in programmes which
involve closer contact and consultation with small farmers
is virtually certain. The main issues are: 1) the size of
this cost and 2) the benefits which might arise by incurring
it.

As to the size, information is, unfortunately, rather
scanty, and a great deal more research needs to be directed
to this issue. A very rough estimate of the recurrent costs
of the agricultural field services (from District Agricultural
Officer downwards) in five Indian states[1] indicated that
they accounted for about 18 to 23 per cent of annual recurrent
expenditure on agriculture. A figure of 30 per cent has been
mentioned for Bangladesh. This is a substantial figure
(which needs much closer definition); but it looks less
formidable in relation to total governmental recurrent
expenditure of all types, and in relation to the proportion
of GNP derived from agriculture. Even to double the numbers
of staff at field level (without increasing - perhaps even
reducing! - the staffing levels at State level) would not
weigh very heavily on the national budget, even if additional
training costs are taken into account.

As to potential benefits, the numbers of small farmers
are enormous in Africa and particularly in Asia. Fairly
conservative estimates in Asia would show that farmers with
less than one hectare represent in many countries 60 per cent
to 75 per cent of all farmers, and occupy around 30 per cent
of all land. It must be remembered that percentages of
all land are in a sense distorted by the very large holdings

---

1   Figures obtained personally from Agriculture Departments
    (1977). Figures cover salary, subsistence, travel and
    administrative costs but not major physical investment.

in some regions which consist of marginal grazing. In a
number of countries (India, Indonesia, Bangladesh, Thailand
and others) 40 per cent or more of the rural population are
classified as below the poverty line.

As to benefits, there is evidence that small farmers
(because of family labour intensity) maintain a level of
productivity per acre very near (sometimes slightly above,
sometimes slightly below) the average productivity of larger
farmers. If it could be assumed that additional numbers of
field staff and an alteration in management training and
methods would substantially increase the output of the mass of
small-holdings on 30 per cent of the land, the benefits of
the investment might well outweigh the costs. It is the
suspicion, quite reasonably held, that in fact even the
existing numbers of field staff do not make much impact on
productivity (larger farmers can get on by themselves; small
ones receive little benefit) which may be at the root of
reluctance to expand.

Here other factors enter - the management of field staffs,
the question whether the existing ratio of staff to farmers is
below a critical level for effective action, the efficiency
of delivery of credit and inputs, the technical content of
programmes, the suitability of research.

POLICY INITIATIVES AND FAILURES

The argument (*Carey Jones* - above) that governments
deliberately direct benefits primarily to influential
supporters, at least in a crude form, is certainly not
universally valid. There have been, and are now, many
governments which, by different processes of reasoning, have
endeavoured, with considerable persistence, to reach the
poorer sections of the agricultural communities and to small
and marginal farmers. Tanzania, India, Indonesia and Sri
Lanka are some of many examples outside the Communist regimes.
That these efforts have had limited success - and sometimes
failure - does not deny their existence. Several other
factors account largely for poor results. At worst, the stated
intention to reach the poor may indeed be mere verbiage -
electoral or dictatorial propaganda in search of mass or
'grass roots' political support. In somewhat more genuine
cases, expenditure and new administrative arrangements for
poverty programmes may indeed by made, yet without any
vigorous or sustained effort to remedy major abuses and
inequities in the political economy - corruption (both
political and administrative), maldistribution of land, and
inequitable tenure. But perhaps the most important remediable
causes of failure are: 1) a failure to recognise that
apparently democratic institutions - for example co-operatives
- can be, and are captured by the richer and more influential
local dominants; 2) a mixture of inefficient management and
real poverty of infrastructure which fails to deliver
effective services to that large proportion of farmers who
have not the power to insist on being served; 3) a failure
to adapt research and technical programmes to the real needs
and potential of small farmers, largely because farmers
are not consulted but presented with programmes devised by
officials and technicians far from the village scene.

9

In Parts II and III below we will consider what are
the requirements for effective contact and service to small
farmers, and how the local political and the administrative
obstacles can be reduced or overcome.

PART II: REQUIREMENTS FOR EFFECTIVE SERVICE TO SMALL FARMERS

THE LOCAL POWER STRUCTURE AND THE CHOICE OF INSTITUTIONS

The reasons why small and marginal farmers need special
attention are well documented and need only the briefest
mention. They are less able to face financial or
social risk. They find it difficult, sometimes unpleasant,
to deal with officials. They are often dependent upon
richer, more influential figures in the village and are
often treated as inferiors. They are sometimes ignorant,
not of their existing land and circumstances, but of new
technical or earning potential. They are very frequently
neglected by Extension staff. They are often suspicious
not only of strangers, but of each other.

For all these reasons, they need a special degree
of encouragement and continuing support. The burden of
this Part II is to consider the various institutions and
initiatives through which effective contact, organisation
and support can be designed.

a) The Extension Service

Criticism of the coverage and management of the Extension
Service has been widespread, and a number of comments on
this subject were received. By no means all of this
criticism reflects on individual officers at field-level,
or on the performance of the Service in promoting a
good technical innovation to large or medium-sized farmers.
Much of the trouble arises, in relation to small and
marginal farmers, from the very situation in which so
many Extension staff work. Expected as they are to meet
targets of technical improvement, and often overburdened

11

with both field and office duties, often without
adequate transport, they naturally visit those farmers
who are most likely to adopt a programme. They have
little time to visit or consult with small farmers, and
little expectation of benefit from such visits.

Further, the management of the Service often leaves
much to be desired. *R.J.G. Steele* comments vigorously
on this management issue:

> Decentralisation of the Ministry of Agriculture
> is the essential prerequisite, even in a very
> small country like Lesotho. Real delegation
> of power should motivate senior District Staff,
> who should be made responsible for failure and
> given credit for success. In my limited
> experience it has been very difficult to get
> middle level supervisors to take their res-
> ponsibilities seriously. I believe this is due
> to their immediate superiors not holding them
> accountable; but they in turn do not have
> authority to take action, and so incompetence
> passes unchecked. I may appear rather author-
> itarian on this point, but it is most damaging
> to the morale of the service if blatant laziness
> and sometimes dishonesty are allowed to continue
> without sanction. Good performance should like-
> wise be commended publicly.

Steele goes on to mention that serious shortage of
transport, and often very poor housing, constantly attack
Service morale. They have often been treated as a purely
technical service (as their name implies), and their
training has not inclined them to consult farmers to
help them to organise themselves, or to look for alternative options to the limited 'package' which they have
to deliver. *H.M. Mathur* strongly suggests that the
retraining of middle level staffs who control or support
the field services, is of high priority.

Steele's reference to 'alternative options' raises
a point about the technical package delivered to farmers
(large and small) which will be mentioned later. But it

is worth mentioning here that the adoption of the (Benor) Training and Visit system of Extension management, although it can greatly improve the regularity of service and the allocation of weekly tasks, is, in practice and despite the intention of the author of the system, very apt to deliver, through 'Contact Farmers' identical packages to small and large farmers alike. What modifications of existing Extension Service and training should be made must await discussion of some other institutional and service systems.

b) Formal co-operatives

Whatever institution is entrusted with responsibility for contact and service to small farmers, some organisation or grouping of farmers as a receiving system is administratively essential. Almost all developing countries have, for longer or shorter periods, looked to the co-operative as the prime tool for this purpose, although some have preferred the Farmers' Association (Taiwan, Malaysia). Indeed, a fully developed and commercial multi-purpose co-operative is, in a sense, an alternative method of organising services - input supplies, credit provision and recovery, storage, marketing services - which, in the absence of a co-operative, have to be covered by government or parastatal organisations. In some areas these are capable of great financial and developmental success. But such successes seem to be concentrated in areas already quite far advanced in commercial development and skills. In less developed areas (whether in Asia or Africa), the remark that 'co-operatives are for big men' is apt to be heard, and active participation in their management by smaller men is minimal.

A rather deeper analysis of the essential nature of co-operatives (in Africa) comes from *Goran Hyden*. His

first point is that co-operatives were born not out of
general goodwill or socialist theory, but out of a dire
necessity - a lifeline for groups threatened with
catastrophe from market forces; and that they have
succeeded mainly in those places where such necessity
pressed upon them. Secondly, he emphasises that co-
operatives were and are a capitalist institution,
concerned with selling and competing in the market;
where this European institution was transferred intact
to developing countries it met with a very different
environment, in which the bulk of the poor were only
marginally in the market economy at all. He writes:

> This does not mean that co-operatives have
> failed as business organisations in these
> countries. In fact, their business record
> is oftentimes quite impressive, particularly
> in areas where the market economy is well-
> established and social behaviour adapted
> according to its demands. One finds invar-
> iably, however, that the driving force behind
> these co-operative successes is a core of
> relatively well-to-do farmers. There is no
> evidence that the co-operative in the rural
> areas of the Third World has been able to
> serve as an instrument of the poor. The
> reason for this is not too difficult to find.
> As a means to incorporate rural producers into
> the modern economy the co-operative has proved
> particularly attractive and important to those
> with the strongest inclinations and greatest
> capacity to move in that direction. Thus, it
> has become the tool of rural entrepreneurs.
> The argument that these people are using the
> co-operatives to exploit the majority of the
> rural producers is too simple. It must be
> recognized that it is primarily to them that
> the co-operative makes a difference. They
> have a stake in it to a much greater extent
> than the ordinary peasant producer who still
> might stand with only one of his legs in the
> market economy. He tends to be a more reluctant
> participant in co-operative business affairs.[1]

---

1   Goran Hyden, 'Cooperation and the poor', *Rural
    Development Participation Review*, Cornell University,
    1980.

And again:

> Establishment of special co-operatives for the
> rural poor is likely to be a far more difficult
> exercise unless some form of political conscious-
> ness exists or can be developed among the
> potential members. Co-operatives in themselves
> are not bringing about greater equality but are
> the vehicles of social action based on certain
> types of consciousness. John Saul (1981)[1] draws
> this conclusion quite firmly after having
> studied the co-operatives in Tanzania.

There is, however unfortunately, abundant evidence from
Africa, Asia and Latin America that the formal co-operative
*as an institution through which active participation and
full benefit can be induced for small and marginal farmers*
is very rarely successful. Indeed, the adoption of this
tool as the *initial* way of providing small farmer service
has been at the cost of failure in many countries for
this particular purpose. A time may come when small
farmers, after gaining more self-confidence by experience
of running their own affairs through other methods, may
be able to play a rewarding part in a large co-operative.
Meanwhile, they are all too often 'passengers' in an
organisation in which the richer and more influential
members virtually monopolise the benefits. Even India,
which has used co-operatives so widely, had to recognise
this and create special agencies to reach small farmers
and the poor.

At a later stage we shall discuss the role of
elected local councils and development committees. But
it is worth noting here that a similar capture of these
institutions by their strongest members is always likely.

---

1   John S. Saul, 'Marketing Cooperatives', in P. Worsley
    (ed), *Two Blades of Grass,* Manchester University Press,
    1971.

c) Small, functional groups

Almost any multi-purpose institution which any member of
the whole local community may join (co-operative) or
elect (council) is likely to recapitulate the local
power structure. It is partly for this reason that
experiments with smaller, single-function groups have
considerable importance: joint and active participation
in the use of a single well, or irrigation channel, a
milk collection scheme, a credit and savings group,
attracting only those immediately concerned, may work
well for a group of small farmers and is small enough
for them to manage themselves. Small groups, whether
of farmers or of weavers, or for almost any productive
or social purpose, are in fact being increasingly used
perhaps mainly by voluntary organisations but also in
government-administered projects. The need to give
them some legal personality for some purposes (especially
for credit) can be quite easily overcome by registration
where necessary. There are, indeed, some difficulties
to overcome. *Gilbert Etienne* points out that the poor
'are not easily "clubable"', because they are often in
competition with each other, often divided by class or
caste, and with differing allegiances. Part of this
objection can be avoided by the very formation of the
group round a specific function in which all are
interested. *Niels Röling* adds that 'natural groups'
(emerging from traditional customs) are not often homo-
geneous in the sense of identical occupations, status
and wealth.

However, the issue is obviously not one of organising
all the poor in a group but of several small groups
each built round a function; and here their common
opportunity and interest may be enough to overcome some
heterogeneity. It may well be that small groups will
(if successful) tend to grow larger or to merge into

some formal co-operative organisation later on; but
this should not be assumed from the start.

Roger King in a study of Nigerian co-operative
systems, adds a practical illustration. In relation to
co-operative effort by *small groups* (about twenty
members) he writes:

> Encouraging this sort of basic co-operation
> requires a very different approach to the part
> of government officials. Groups need to be
> based on specific local needs which the case
> study showed can be quite different even in
> neighbouring villages. To be sensitive to
> these needs it is necessary to involve the
> rural population in decisions about which
> activities a new group should undertake and
> how they should undertake it. The government
> co-operative department would then support
> rather than direct co-operative activity.
> This approach is quite the reverse of that in
> the case study, where top-down planning
> resulted in each co-operative being offered
> the same package and being required to adhere
> to identical rules.[1]

d) Special organising staff

Neither normal Extension staff nor co-operatives have
either the clear responsibility or the training for a
genuinely consultative approach to small and marginal
farmers, which might encourage them to express their
problems, to organise themselves, and to play an active
part in managing their own programmes (with technical
support and some facilitation of their contacts with
officials). It is the recognition of this situation
which has led to experiments in the use of 'group

---

1 Roger King, 'Co-operative policy in peasant societies:
  the case of Nigeria', Second Co-operative Seminar,
  Plunkett Foundation, September 1977.

organisers' or 'institution officers' or 'facilitators'.[1]
FAO, some universities and some voluntary agencies have
usually initiated this additional, catalysing activity,
to fill an obvious gap. As in the case of voluntary
agency work (see following section) this at present can
only be done on a small scale. But insofar as it is
effective, it can at least serve as a pointer to the kind
of training and the methods of approach needed in the
national Extension Services.

e) Voluntary organisations

The relatively small scale on which voluntary organisations
can at present contribute to national effort is obvious.
A further common difficulty, particularly in agriculture,
can arise from their technical weakness; often they
cannot afford the professional staff needed. This can
be remedied by close collaboration with government staff,
although this is not always evident. It is therefore
from the quality of their work rather than its range
that some lessons for wider action can be learned.

These qualities can include: 1) a genuine concern
to serve the weaker sections; 2) usually much less
transitory staffing than in government service - thus
more time and care can be spent in developing personal
relations and trust; 3) much more flexibility in action,
since they are not bound by pre-selected programmes and
regulations as the bureaucracy is; 4) economy, and a
concentration on using local resources and energies;
5) quicker decision, made locally.

---

1 For example, in some Asian Survey on Agricultural and
  Rural Research and Development (ASARRD) programmes
  (eg Thailand); in Sri Lanka (Gala Oyo) and Bangladesh
  and Nepal. 'Facilitators' are recommended by Bruce
  Johnston and W.C. Clark. Similar work is recommended
  by D. Thakar (Indian Institute of Management, Ahmedabad).

It is evident that these five qualities set standards
which are extremely hard to achieve in national development,
implying elements of devolution, local concern, staff
training and posting which constantly show up as failures
on the national scale.

There is a host of ways in which voluntary organisations
may appear on the rural scene - from individuals within
a local community; from religious and other organisations,
whether indigenous or as branches of international move-
ments; from what may be called 'donors', including
universities and other socially - or developmentally -
oriented institutions, indigenous or foreign; from
experiments sponsored by UN agencies (eg FAO, WHO).
There are also a host of variations in their approach
to their work. Insofar as each or any of them share
the five qualities listed above (and most of them share
many), they should be treated as a source of experiments
and of inspiration to the larger agencies, including
governments, concerned in rural development. In the
particular field covered by this Occasional Paper - the
widening of the flow of benefits to the poor and the
strengthening of genuine participation - their work has
peculiar relevance and value. There is a fast growing
number of examples, too long to quote here.

Robert Chambers admirably summarises the main issue:

> Both for promoting demand from below, and for
> linking resources and the poor, there is the
> eternal problem of spreading on a larger scale
> what can be made to work on a small-scale, of
> the shift from the voluntary agency to the
> government department, of the transfer from
> committed leadership to routine administration.
> It is here that the two approaches are strongly
> complementary, and give cause, I think, for
> hope. For if the poorer people have or can be
> given rights over natural resources, and if
> they know that they have those rights, then
> their demands may offset the slippage towards
> the rural elite which would otherwise occur.

There is also the approach (which colleagues
here have been exploring) of intermediate or
hybrid organisations, supported by government,
operating on a larger scale than normal
voluntary agencies, but retaining their con-
viction and flexibility.

f) *'Self-help'*

Self-help organisations, in which a local community sets
itself the task of building an access road or a school
(even in 'Village College' in Kenya), or a bridge or a
clean water supply, a cattle dip or an irrigation
channel, have all the characteristics of active involve-
ment in both labour and monetary contribution. Although
the effort is usually organised by a leading local
citizen (and occasionally the road leads to his house),
in many cases rich and poor alike gain. It is partly an
offspring from community development ideas, in which
some technical help and materials are expected to come
from government sources, but may also exist (as in Kenya's
'Harambee' effort) as a local, although officially
blessed, effort in which all sections of the people may
contribute and benefit. It can generate, at least
temporarily, much local enthusiasm and some capital gain
to the nation. But it is usually a 'one-off' effort,
more often concerned with local social infrastructure,
and therefore cannot be classed as an agricultural
development system.[1]

---

1 For a full discussion of Kenyan experience in this
  field (and for several able articles on agricultural
  administration in East Africa) see David K. Leonard
  (ed) *Rural Administration in Kenya,* East African
  Literature Bureau, Management and Administration
  Series, No 2, Nairobi 1973.

Combatting the effects of the local power structure

The foregoing paragraphs have run through briefly most
of the important ways of contact with and organisation
of small farmers. It is evident that several of them,
unfortunately the most widely used, do not fulfil the
requirements of a method which would be likely to
ensure an easy and widespread response. Moreover, it
is not only a question of goodwill in the central
government, important as that is. Let us assume that
the government of India established the Small Farmer
Development Agency, the Drought-prone Area Programme,
the Marginal Farmer and Landless Agency, and the Integrated
Rural Development Programme in good faith - as I personally believe. Let us assume also that the installation
of democratic, elected committees at village, block and
district level (Panchayats) was in good faith - and
indeed in democratic idealism - as I believe it certainly
was. Yet these committees and programmes have been
partially captured by local power-holders - though they
have reached a substantial number of the poor. The
point to be made here is that the assumption - indeed
the fact - of central goodwill in some countries is not
enough to achieve adequate benefit to the rural poor,
unless additional and, indeed, subtle measures are taken
to neutralise or evade local exploitation or, in other
words, to breach the prevailing local social pattern of
relations.

A word is needed about 'capture of benefits'. This
is often treated as a deliberate act of obstruction or
exclusion; and there are indeed some shocking cases of
this. But there are other, and less sinister, factors
involved. The first lies in the bare fact that more
powerful people have more access to and more influence
with the sources of supply. If supplies are short, or
late or faulty, they can needle officials effectively;

the poor cannot. Secondly, the content of a scheme may
be such that the poor dare not take the risks of adoption:
to risk one acre out of two, with a credit debt, is a
far greater risk, with less chance of recovery from
failure, than to risk three acres out of twenty. Nevertheless, the poor find it very hard to organise themselves to exert effective pressure. They are in
competition with each other, and the nature of their
dependency on the more powerful makes it difficult and
economically dangerous for them to challenge the village
establishment or officials. In conflict situations
they feel themselves to be the weaker side. If outsiders urge them to take risks, they will want to be
sure that support will be both present and effective
if a crunch comes.[1] Outsiders (including Extension
staff) have to be aware of this situation; and no doubt
schemes which enhance the capacity of the poor with a
minimum of direct challenge will stand more chance of
success.

The danger of over-emphasising the capture of
benefits by the rich - and thereby neglecting other
common reasons for failure - is mentioned by *S.K. Rao*
and *N.K. Jaiswal*:

> The other assumption that the dominant socio-
> political forces at local level are defeating
> the purpose of development efforts for the
> rural poor could sometimes be over-emphasised.
> The effect is that other factors lose their
> gravity. For example, in India, the milch
> cattle distribution programmes, or handicrafts
> or cottage industries projects, quite often
> fail due to inadequate project assessment at
> the feasibility and appraisal stage, discordant
> management of input supply, and inadequate

---

1 Cf W.H. and Charlotte Wiser, *Behind Mud Walls*,
Berkeley, Los Angeles 1963, for a description of
the multiple fears which beset the poor. Also Paul
Devitt in *Extension, Planning and the Poor*, Occasional
Paper No 2, ODI, 1977.

stream marketing of the output. But external
factors/forces including local power structure
are often adduced as plausible arguments as an
excuse for this deficiency.

B.F. Johnston and *W.C. Clark*[1] mention the danger of an
over-suspicious attitude to local 'leaders':

> A second reason for the neglect of leadership
> issues is ideological. It is well known and
> hardly surprising that effective leaders at
> all levels of development organization tend
> to be drawn from the more progressive, better
> educated and often relatively better off strata
> of rural society. (See, for example, Korten
> 1980.) We have already called attention to
> foreign advisers' often uncritical advocacy
> of superficially democratic and egalitarian
> forms of organization. In the present context,
> this advocacy often amounts to a hostility
> towards the emergence of forceful, innovative
> leadership. It emphasises instead a vague
> blend of local (leaderless) autonomy plus
> 'professional' (read 'central' or 'imported')
> program management. Such a simplistic attitude
> is precisely the opposite of what is needed to
> achieve practical results.

The argument goes on to suggest that an answer lies
in 'a productive balance between the facilitation and
the control of leadership behaviour'. Alas, this is not
so much an answer as a restatement of the difficulty -
by whom and how is this balance to be struck and enforced?
Honest and unselfish leadership may indeed exist in
some cases, and should not be discouraged. But to rely
on it generally is not enough to prevent widespread
failure. The effort in this Occasional Paper is to
suggest institutional and organisational approaches
which 1) reduce the likelihood of benefit capture and
2) seek to build up the self-confidence of the poorer
sections to manage more of their own affairs themselves.

---

1   In a draft of *Redesigning Rural Development* (forth-
    coming from Johns Hopkins University Press).

Despite these qualifications, the deeply engrained patterns of socio-political life constitute a most serious obstacle to any easy assumption that better technology or better management can by themselves ensure the growth of a more participative and more equitably rewarded life for the rural poor. If they are more noticeable in Asia, where social hierarchies are more detailed and closely defined, they have grown up also among the modern societies of Tropical Africa and have long been prevalent in Latin America. It is all too easy to think of 'small farmers' as atomised individuals, who can be persuaded to co-operate with each other. But in fact each is imbedded in loyalties - to family, clan, tribe, racial group, patron - and in fears that neglect of this security (such as it is) by behaving as clubable individuals for some new economic purpose may lead to disaster. It is against this background that we need to consider some suggestions by which the risks of capture can be minimised.

Quite a number of such suggestions are put forward. We have suggested that small special-purpose groups are less likely to attract capture than whole-village organisations. *Robert Chambers* has emphasised the possibility of channelling assets directly to the ownership of the poor - eg a bamboo-tube well, an IHP pump. *Tendler* has suggested that some social benefits, often already available to the well-off, provoke less competition from them. She also remarks that some powerful infrastructure organisations, eager to expand their operations, may provide structures and services which in fact benefit large numbers of the poor as well as the rich.[1] *Gilbert Etienne* rightly stresses that shortages of supply are often the precipitating cause

---

1 Eg the Kenya Land Development Organisation.

of unequal benefit; the rich will be first come and
first served. The same applies to attractive subsidies;
scarce and subsidised supplies create the greatest
temptation of all. If chemical fertiliser is too
expensive to import in adequate quantity, extension
packages should be changed rather than the poor
excluded.

Another suggestion, though more difficult to
handle, must be recorded. *Tendler* also mentions that
in some circumstances 'you may do better for the poor
with strong, centrally managed, non-participatory
projects, if "participation" turns out to mean "control
by the elites"'. This thought is echoed by *J. Jacobs*:

> The paper states that 'without devolution the
> rest fails'. It goes on to indicate some of
> the factors in most developing countries
> which inhibit or even prohibit this devolution.
> I do not share the author's confidence that
> 'localism' is the key to the development of
> the rural poor. In the majority of the poor
> nations, the greatest development took place
> concurrently with the maximum centralism. I
> would suggest that the key to the development
> of the rural poor is rather the convincing of
> the urban affluent that it is in their own
> interests to bring about this development.
> Localism may in the event be one of the tools
> capable of bringing about that development.

These two comments do not undermine the critical
importance of decentralisation if the poor are to be
intelligently served. But they do emphasise timing
and some discrimination between subjects and programmes.
The Government of India deliberately retained initial
financial (and some administrative) control of the
special agencies, partly for speed of execution, but
also precisely to avoid local capture of benefits at
State or District level, whether by politicians or
Panchayats. In doing so, they hoped to take a step
which would increase the self-confidence and security

of the poor. Even so, they did not wholly succeed,
and quite a lot of benefits reached unintended hands.
Such precautionary action may well be needed elsewhere.
As to discrimination, there are indeed some large
projects (particularly some forms of infrastructure)
in which village-level participation may not be helpful
in early stages. But in the end, services have to
reach the ground in the village; and at that point local
views and knowledge always matter.

This leads us to a gloomy comment by *A.Z.M. Obaidullah
Khan*.[1] It starts by quoting a UNDP statement:

> The experience of both MFAL[2] and SFDA shows that
> it is not enough to set up an organisation
> catering to a target group without first under-
> taking thorough changes in the social and
> political environment. As long as the village
> remains stratified and dominated by the rich
> groups, it is difficult to implement measures
> which solely cater for the under-privileged.

And he comments:

> The target group approach is in fact a modified
> form of centralised State paternalism which,
> through a dedicated bureaucracy, hopes to
> circumvent the rural power-structure and to
> channel programmes and benefits directly to
> the poor - an example of the triumph of hope
> over experience.

One might comment that it is in the triumph of hope over
experience, if the hope is aware of the dangers, that
human progress makes its way.

It is here that an extremely vigorous contention
must be given a place. It comes from *Janice Jiggins* and

---

1 A.Z.M. Obaidullah Khan, 'Rural Development in South
   Asia', *Asian Affairs*, Vol 3, No 2, June 1981, quoting
   UNDP Evaluation Paper No 2.
2 The Marginal Farmers and Landless Labour Agency.

Niels Röling,[1] with some support in its emphasis on
strengthening local organisations, from *Goran Hyden*:
it doubtless would have much support from many radical
organisations, It is the concept of 'countervailing
power' - that is, basically political and administrative
punch developed within the so-called 'target groups'
of the poor (and here they assume that someone, at
least, perhaps the central government, does regard the
poor as a target, and that someone (an outsider?) helps
the poor to organise), The comment demands neither a
simple top-down nor a simple bottom-up approach, but
action from both ends - a vigorous and efficient
government matched by vigorous and effective counter
thrust from organised and confident local pressure,
Perhaps a brief extract from *Robert Chambers'* comment
should be added:

> Effective demand from below requires deliberate
> fostering. Collective awareness and organisation,
> and action and negotiation by the poor is one
> course. Democratic political processes can help:
> the ballot box is a powerful weapon at some
> times and in some places and should certainly
> not be underestimated in India. But in countries
> with a reasonably independent legal system, the
> courageous and dogged use of the law may be the
> most powerful weapon. In India, for example,
> the land reform legislation, which diligently
> implemented could transform the life of many,
> perhaps most, of the rural poor, is already on
> the statute books. What is needed is a pro-
> longed, brave and detailed campaign to secure
> enforcement.

Precise and limited objectives, such as the law, are
always welcome, and admit of immediate local action. The
wider sweep of a new balance of power in the *Jiggins/Röling*
vision requires that most of the changes discussed in this
Occasional Paper must be achieved - sooner or later.

---

1 From correspondence and a draft paper by Janice Jiggins,
   Niels Röling and Arnoud Budelman, not quotable verbatim.

TECHNOLOGY, RESEARCH, PROGRAMMING

We move now from discussion of institutions for contact
and protection of small farmers to the content and
technology of programmes more deliberately designed
to meet their physical, social and economic needs and
to encourage their active participation in the choice
and execution of such programmes.

The idea that local programmes should emerge from
consultations with very local groups is not a new one.
It is as old as community development (whether in Asia
or Africa), where the ascertainment of 'felt needs'
featured largely in the prospectus. This idea fell
somewhat out of fashion from the mid-1960s to the mid-
1970s. It was overshadowed by the Green Revolution and
by concentration on major projects, for *all* farmers, in
theory, but benefitting the larger ones in practice, in
which the technology and programme content was decided
at central level. It has, however, recently gained new
life from the technical side - from the realisation of
great local variations in what can, technically, be
done in particular villages or village clusters. It
has been accentuated by the movement to push local
planning or programming further down - at first to
District, then to sub-District, and (increasingly) to
village or village clusters; it has been exemplified
in the Daudzai Project[1] (Academy for Rural Development,

---

1 For description see *Agricultural Administration*, Vol
   3, No 6, 1976, and Address to the 2nd International
   Seminar on Change in Agriculture by Shoaid Sultan Khan,
   published in *Policy and Practice in Rural Development*,
   Croom Helm/ODI, London, 1976.

Peshawar, Pakistan), where new programmes for villages
were worked out by consultation, village by village,
by a three-man team of officials with local farmers,
followed by execution by the farmers and continuous
'training' and technical support from the sub-District
level. It is exemplified by a new proposal in
Bangladesh, in which the detailed soil survey of small
areas will be used, as well as other local factors,
in discussion between farmers and a technical (official)
team to settle local programmes, fertiliser requirements,
etc. It is exemplified increasingly in India where
Block Level Planning and detailed discussion of local
needs and potential is spreading very widely. It has
been used very successfully in Botswana.

This type of approach[1] concerns the formal process
of agricultural programming and planning, and, as such,
could become a regular methodology of government action.
There is also a comparable process in the actual execution
of a particular function. It is worth mentioning a
remarkable case of detailed consultation with farmer-
beneficiaries in a Philippine irrigation programme.[2] In
this project consultation was continuous, from the
moment when farmers walked the fields with engineers to
settle the most appropriate alignment of distributaries
and field channels, to final and joint approval of the
whole project layout. There is an important point here
- that 'participation' is not only to be achieved by
creating special agencies or representative bodies or

---

1 I have described this more fully in terms of 'diagnosis'
  and 'prescription' in earlier ODI publications (eg
  Agricultural Development and the Rural Poor) and
  elsewhere.
2 See B. Bagadion and F. Korten with D. Korten, 'Promoting
  participatory management on small irrigation schemes'
  Irrigation Management Network Paper 2/80/2, ODI, 1980.

associations but can and should be treated *as a management method* for use in a wide variety of technical and environmental decisions and execution.

The movement towards far more local consultation, technical assessment and programming has been slow but steady over the last ten years. It was, in the early days, considerably more academic. First, rather theoretical work on District planning; next, a phase when detailed local resource surveys were carried out, often by academic institutions (universities, management institutes, project designers).[1] At that stage it was still some way from operational and technical implementation. It is significant and valuable that this approach, in which farmers are closely involved with local field staff in working out programmes in which both will be actively engaged, is now gaining ground at the operational level and as a management method. If government staffs are to work directly with small farmers and the rural poor, it is probable that schemes of this nature will be the best tool. The work on 'rapid rural appraisal', notably sponsored by the Institute of Development Studies (University of Sussex)[2] has helped this approach by suggesting methods by which the time, cost, and expertise needed for local technical and economic diagnosis can be reduced and brought within the duties of local staff. It is by this diagnosis that the assumption that new production by the poor will be suited to them, marketable and profitable, can be safeguarded.

---

1 For example, the university surveys used for the Special Rural Development Programme in Kenya, or the work in India by the Indian Institute of Management, the Indian Institute of Public Administration, the National Institute of Rural Development, or the Agricultural University of Coimbatore.
2 See *IDS Bulletin* Vol 12, No 4, 1981 and also *Agricultural Administration,* University of Reading, Special Issue, November 1981.

It is worth noting that these developments represent a happy convergence and also strengthening of three approaches to rural development which were previously separated and thereby less effective. First, the community development approach, strong on consultation but weak on technical expertise; second, micro-economic and technical appraisal, strong in its disciplines but costly in time and usually *ex post*; and third, planning, strong at central level but over-generalised for local application. The convergence represents full consultation but supported by economic and technical appraisal; appraisal simplified and *ex ante*; and much more local programming, moving up to sub-District level and towards planning at District and central levels.

On the side of technical research, the work of ICRISAT on very small-scale assessment, consultation, and choice of detailed technology is worth a short illustration. *James G. Ryan* writes (about such action at village level):

> We have again started by discussions at the whole-village level, with the officers of the Department of Agriculture playing a prominent role. Visits to ICRISAT Centre were arranged to inform villagers of the technology and to train them in the use of the improved implements and techniques. Then the 15.4 ha watershed and its occupants were identified and more detailed group discussion ensued. This proved extremely time-intensive but productive. Indeed I feel as coordinator of this project that the investment of this time was essential to ensure that we adequately recognised the constraints facing farmers, such as bullock power (especially small farmers) to drive the wheeled tool-carrier. This exercise was also important for the Department of Agriculture officers who were made aware that we had a range of technology options for consideration by the watershed farmers and not a single 'package of practices'. Hence on-the-job training of these extension officers was and remains an integral component of our approach.

He adds later:

> A team approach by extension staff would
> enhance the consultative approach with
> farmers even more. Having the soil-conser-
> vation officer and the agronomist jointly
> responsible for the watershed program at all
> stages increases the need for consultation
> with farmers at all stages.

By insisting on consultation and on local diagnosis
and prescription, we have added some extra detail to the
list of requirements concerned with the capacity of
service organisations to reach the poor. If, here and
there, a strong expert team carried out a long and
thorough local diagnosis and prescribes accordingly, not
much benefit or guidance to national development tactics
will result - for senior expert personnel are not available for every cluster of villages. Such work can only
be done on a large scale if it is mainly within the
competence and training of local staffs (from the field
assistants up to sub-District) with visits from more
specialised staff from the District level or from a
research station. There are certainly some implications
as to recurrent costs, and above all training costs, if
these operational cadres are to be strengthened to a
level of competence equal to the task of diagnosis (which
does not recur often) and support (which must be continuous).

Adaptation of research and technology

If the process of local consultation with farmers, diagnosis
and joint identification of possible programmes, and
small-scale organisation, is to be followed by technical
action, the range of alternatives available to the field
staff, ultimately from research, will have to be wider.
The objective of small farmers in particular is likely
to be intensification of production in their very small
area, with a clear hope of worthwhile increase in income.

This may well point to crop diversification, in ways which
might not be worthwhile to larger farmers with paid
labour, and not necessarily on pure stands of cereal
crops. It will also be constrained by a need to keep
purchased inputs to a very moderate level, to reduce
financial risk. Not only economic (farm management)
research but also the availability of suitable crop
varieties and small-scale technology (eg the IHP pump
or bamboo-tubewell) will be needed; an example for a
single situation evolved by ICRISAT has already been
mentioned.

Economy in cash inputs, sharing of facilities,
hardy varieties, perhaps able to resist water-stress,
intercropping or relay cropping, minor investment on
levelling, draining, fencing, etc may all be needed to
fit the small farmer's situation. The dominance of a
policy of high inputs for high yields, the emphasis on
staple food production, well suited to larger farms,
may not in many cases be the right answer where only
two acres or even less is available. Subsidiary activities to raise income (eg small animals, vegetable
production, etc) may all add significantly to very low
cash incomes. Most of these possible remedies are well
known; but the modifications of research effort needed
to put them to widespread use have been very slow to
materialise. Even adaptive research stations too often
have been limited to fairly mechanical crop-trials to
do the donkey-work of research testing of local soil
responses, initiated by the major research institutions,
without much adaptation to farmer needs.

SUPPLY TO SMALL FARMERS

Only a brief mention of systems of supply of credit,
physical inputs, and certain urgent services (such
as pest-control or veterinary services) is needed in
the special context of small farmers; and that is to
underline its extreme importance. Better-off farmers
can exert considerable pressure on officials, bank
managers or supply organisations to get their fair
share (or more) of supplies; small farmers cannot.
Yet timely credit and inputs are desperately needed
by them; indeed, there is field evidence to show that
they value this even more than technical advice. If
they can get the money and fertiliser many feel that
they could do their farming job as well as, or better
than, a junior Extension Officer can suggest. If they
fail to get it in time, the whole previous effort of
contact, organisation and programming is largely wasted
and discredited, and the morale of field staff sinks.

The principal reasons why fertiliser, seed and
credit so often arrive late or in inadequate quantity
lie, firstly, in the general weakness of physical infrastructure in poor countries - railway locomotives,
trucks, roads, storate depots - ie the inadequate
investment in a key function. This can only slowly be
remedied. The second reason lies in the weakness of
the final retail distribution network. Demand for
small quantities of varied materials from villages
outside the network of feeder roads is not attractive
to private enterprise; and while a parastatal should
have no difficulty in bulk purchase and wholesale

distribution, the necessary fine network of retail
distribution is often lacking or very inefficient,
Even co-operatives often find it commercially unprofit-
able to maintain stocks within reasonably easy access
of farmers. In the end, small farmers are often driven
to rely both for credit and inputs on small-traders
and moneylenders, who may combine both functions. This
is a problem which affects the whole agricultural
economy and on which renewed management effort and some
additional investment is needed. Failure has persisted
over so many years that governments appear to have
become fatalistically resigned to it.[1]

---

1   Some of this argument on supply is derived from the
    draft of a (forthcoming) FAO paper on 'Delivery
    Systems'.

PART III: ADMINISTRATION

REQUIRED CHANGES IN GOVERNMENT OR ELECTED COUNCIL SERVICES

Up to this point we have mentioned or implied a number of
changes in government policy and management.

a) A considerable change in the training and management
of field services to take into account a new
constituency with special needs.

b) A revaluation of institutional choices, to protect
the flow of benefits towards small and marginal
farmers.

c) A modification of research and technological effort.

d) Some restructuring of planning and programming
systems to make more room for locale-specificity
and local consultative choices.

e) A strengthening of the delivery system, with
special emphasis on final retail distribution and
on logistical infrastructure.

By no means all of these changes involve heavy new
expenditure: a) requires some extra personnel and e) some
extra expenditure on transport, communications, and storage
- physical investment. But the remainder concern modifications of existing structures, changes in the content of
the work of existing personnel and in their training, and
a certain, difficult, change in attitude.

The nature of governmental effort - bureaucratic style

There has always been grave doubt whether bureaucratic
action by itself could hope to achieve genuine rural
development. The only possible hope has been that it could

help to generate and support, perhaps with the aid of
democratic local institutions, a more dynamic, participatory
effort by the people themselves. But perhaps the very style
of bureaucratic action and attitudes stands in the way.
The 'top-down' syndrome runs right through the services to
the most junior member. It is not only that the junior
staff are tied down to preconceived programmes in which
they have had little or no say; it is not only that their
immediate superiors look for obedience from them rather
than initiative either from them or from the farmers; they
themselves tend to feel in a superior position to the small
and poor farmers whom they should serve. Combined with
the normal suspicion which villagers feel towards any
government official (though they may hope to exploit them
if possible), the attitudes on both sides are not conducive
to participation, let alone self-management by farmers in
their own programmes.

Speaking from East Africa, *Goran Hyden* has some hard
things to say on this issue:

> The local nature of farming systems, however,
> raises both the need for more research along the
> lines of how they can be developed and the question
> of how central governments can deal with these
> situations. Maybe they aren't suited for the
> extension task at all. The task could in some
> cases perhaps be better handled by other
> organizations which have adopted a specific
> mandate to deal with the poor. It is my view
> as expressed in the book *Beyond Ujamaa in Tanzania*
> (Heinemann 1980) that in a predominantly small-
> holder system of agricultural production, as found
> in Africa, which depends on a very simple
> technology, the opportunities for state interventions
> are almost nil, as these systems of production
> aren't really dependent on outside support for
> their own reproduction. Any development of
> these small production units has to come from
> efforts that are more closely associated with the
> day-to-day existence within these units than a
> government bureaucrat is.

Hyden adds later:

> There is plenty of room for manoeuvre here provided
> government leaders realize and accept that much of
> what governments now do in a terribly unreliable
> and inefficient manner can be carried out much
> better by NGOs and voluntary community efforts (of
> education, health, marketing, etc). I believe an
> increasing number of people in prominent positions
> around Africa are beginning to accept this point
> which isn't revolutionary, yet fundamental for the
> future of development on the continent.

The 'inefficient and unreliable manner' (with its effects
on cost-efficiency) is by no means only due to the attitudes
or performance of Extension staff, but also in large measure
to failures in the supply system, and to unsuitable programmes;
but the failure to consult farmers is due to Extension
training, or, where there is some consultation, inability to
modify official instructions. Voluntary organisations do
indeed have many virtues at the contact level. But, at least
at present, they are too small and too few to undertake the
national task. At present there is no realistic alternative
to the use of government services, retrained as far as
possible to a more consultative style, using voluntary
agencies where they can, and indeed seeking to get nearer to
the example of the best of these agencies.

Without contradicting, and indeed sharing Hyden's wish
that voluntary agencies of various kinds, could increase
their range, their liaison with, and support from the
government,[1] it would seem that in practice a steady effort
to alter the style and training of governmental service
might bring the most widespread results. In this connection,

---

1 *Robert Chambers* mentions a possible initiative by the
   Indian Government to develop a joint scheme with voluntary
   organisations over a considerable area, and there are a
   number of other schemes (eg in the 'Peer Group' programme
   associated with the Agricultural University of Udaipar
   or the Bangladesh schemes involving joint initiatives
   of the Bangladesh Bank and the government services.)

the work of *David C. Korten* from the Asian Institute of
Management, and of the Rural Development Committee,
Cornell University,[1] under the leadership of *Norman
Uphoff*, need special mention.

These two authors (both of whom commented most
helpfully by letters and drafts) have published numerous
papers on the subject,[2] and in terms of practical action,
Korten has worked with the National Irrigation Authority
in the Philippines on practical training of irrigation
staff for a new style of approach, and has hopes of
similar work on forestry. In terms of action research,
Uphoff has produced an extremely interesting report[3]
recording the success and some precise field problems of
the Institutional Organiser approach in the joint Agricultural Research and Training Institute/Cornell University
water development project in Gala Oyo, Sri Lanka.

All this work (carried out in the three years 1980
to 1982) which is beginning to show results of field
trials of participation-theory not merely as a critique
of existing bureaucratic style but as assessment of
their trials of new methods, when it is added to the
large documentation of voluntary organisational work in
a large number of countries, together make a strong case
for further experiment on a larger scale, entailing a
policy decision; *Robert Chambers* has mentioned the possibility of such a programme in India.

---

1   The Rural Development Committee, Cornell University
    also publish the quarterly *Rural Development Partici-
    pation Review*.
2   See, for example, D.C. Korten and N.T. Uphoff, 'Bureau-
    cratic reorientation for rural development'; D.C.
    Korten and F.B. Alfonso (eds), *Bureaucracy and the Poor*,
    McGraw-Hill International, Singapore, 1981; also their
    papers on 'Community organisation and rural development',
    Public Administration Review, September/October 1980;
    and their 'Agricultural planning and management for
    rural development', Asian Institute of Management,
    February 1982.
3   Published by the Agricultural Research and Training
    Institute, Colombo, 26 March 1982.

Modification of the bureaucratic approach is not only
a matter of training; there are structural, institutional
and management realignments involved, which are considered
later.

Elected councils

While these systems of direct contact between officials
and small farmers do need to rely on the formation of some
grouping of the farmers concerned, they do not depend upon
formally elected councils; they are more likely to use a
purely functional group or possibly a 'pre-co-operative'
or more formal primary co-operative, usually formed for a
single purpose. But this solution is not satisfactory to
many governments, who believe strongly that local democratic
institutions are absolutely essential to guide and check
officials and to mobilise popular energies. Democratic,
elected councils, possibly at several levels, are therefore
given development responsibilities usually both for
agriculture and for social services of many kinds. Such
councils may be primarily used to needle and humanise the
bureaucracy in their area, or to use their political
influence to assist governmental schemes. They may be given
some sources of revenue, with corresponding powers to execute
small schemes, either with their own or with governmental
seconded staff. But there may be councils at a higher level
to whom major powers and taxing authority have been devolved
by statute.

It is not easy to quote any system of this kind which
has proved to be fully satisfactory, particularly as far as
full representation of the poor is concerned. It is indeed
possible, and often said, that they have never been given a
proper chance to succeed - good staffing and adequate
finance under their own control - because the central

government and nervous civil servants (especially in the Treasury!) have kept their wings clipped.[1] Even if there is truth in this, such councils do seem to suffer two weaknesses in particular. First, they are apt to belabour government for greatly increased spending on social services (schools, clinics, subsidies of many kinds) while largely shirking the difficult problems of increasing production from local resources, let alone the problems of production disciplines (water dues, credit recovery, disease control, soil conservation).[2] Secondly, the larger councils (sub-District, District) offer ready-made opportunities of political influence, patronage and economic advantages to the leadership. This is unavoidable; but it is worth remembering that, in the administration of social services in rural areas, the leadership is not usually in such direct competition with the weaker sections as they are in credit-allocation, irrigation distribution, investment subsidies, access to services.

Small, face-to-face 'councils' at village level can be the most genuinely democratic, and indeed most villages have had various ways in which village affairs were managed (systems for conflict-resolution, use of wells, sanitation, clearing paths, etc). Attempts to graft agricultural development onto these functions have been tried in many countries. In Bangladesh, the 'Gram Sarkar' (village government) appears to envisage a cluster of special associations (youth groups, women's groups, farmer groups, etc), each of which is represented in the Sarkar. It seems to be difficult to graft on activities accompanied by monetary benefits, subsidies, etc, which are non-traditional and a cause of jealousies and power conflicts; and it may be that a number of small functional groups, which may later grow to larger and more formal co-operatives at a

1 Local government in Kenya was at one time starved in this way, and later, because of resulting failures, it was robbed of many of its functions on grounds of 'inefficiency

2 For example, in the Dandzai project (Pakistan) the first response from villages consulted was for services. This demand was gently deflected into willing co-operation in land, irrigation and road improvements in aid of agriculture

higher level, is a possible alternative to the all-
embracing village council. Further, development of more
genuinely democratic leadership and self-confidence
within the village may be a necessary preliminary to the
establishment of larger councils in which the interests
of poorer sections will be more vigorously represented.

Tendler has two comments on the foregoing paragraph.
First, it may well be that schools and clinics are what
the people want and demand, and that councils are right
to press for them - evidence from Nigeria is quoted, and
it could be found in many countries. It may well be that
villagers know that a social service surely can be provided,
whereas production improvements are far more difficult and
risky. The second comment is to agree that competition
with the poor is less strong and direct in the case of
social services than in production facilities (subsidies,
credit, access to scarce inputs). The conclusion from
both these comments would seem to suggest that to allocate
some social functions to councils may well be desirable,
on several grounds.

It can be said that, at least in India, a strong belief
persists that whole-village councils, and indeed councils
at higher levels, with wide development responsibilities,
are a democratic necessity, particularly in the longer
term. *S.K. Rau* and *N.K. Jaiswal* write:

> The local institutions like Cooperatives and
> Panchayats have by no means withered away nor
> become pernicious. It would be forsaking all
> the present to postulate that direct contact
> with the rural poor by way of consultation,
> stimulation and continued support could be
> achieved only by some agency not involved in the
> hierarchical structure and relationship of local
> society. Any attempt to create organisations
> parallel to local Panchayat or which bypass or
> ignore it, cannot be successful in the long run
> for a country which has chosen a particular path

of democratic process for the whole country.
Though due to some forces which always work as
a churning process it could be that such
organisations show results in some aspects
only . . . there is also the need for organising
special purpose cooperatives and functional
groups for artisans, weavers, irrigation groups,
etc, for taking care of the special interests
of the weaker sections. But such institutions
must have the patronage of local Panchayats.

This point of view is strongly supported by the
present Secretary to the Ministry of Rural Reconstruction
in Delhi:[1]

One of the points of criticism against the Panchayati Raj institutions has been their domination
by socio-economically stronger groups. This,
however, is an intermediate phase. The political
logic of articulation and intermediate aggregation has wider ramifications and improves the
sense of solidarity among the weaker sections.
It is aided by dynamic elements of competitive
politics and leads to periodic shifting of elites
and changes in the traditional power structure
better aligned with growing strengths of the
poverty groups. Thus in *the long run* {my italics}
the development of these institutions is bound to
accelerate the processes of politicalisation, democratisation and conscientisation of the rural poor.

Despite this long-run political vision, there is a
good deal of anxiety about the *short-run* performance over
the last ten years; and these doubts are also felt even in
India. *H.M. Mathur*[2] writes:

The community development programme of 1950s was
based on the premise that the village communities
were closely knit, harmonious entities and that
in response to exhortations of the Community Development officials all people from the villages
would come out to build roads, schools, wells, tanks
and other community assets. It was believed that
people would work together and equitably share in
the benefits of development. Planners visualised a
'Panchayati Raj' and under the scheme of democratic

1 S.C. Varma, *India's Attack on Rural Poverty*, New Delhi,
   1981. This is a very valuable overview.
2 H.M. Mathur, 'Rural development in traditional societies:
   an anthropological approach'. Paper for the Symposium
   on Rural Development in S. Asia Intercongress IAUES,
   Amsterdam, April 1981.

decentralization they devolved responsibility for
local development to the village leaders. What
happened to the Panchayati Raj which was introduced
with a great fanfare to bring development and people
closer together was described some time ago in the
following terms: 'When Panchayati Raj came great
hopes were aroused and it was expected that Panchayats
would be in a position to involve all the people in
local efforts to build the village community on a
pattern in which disparities would quickly vanish.
But the people who were elected later arranged
themselves into strong warring factions, usually
along the caste lines. Soon they became so busy
in fighting among themselves - not always on issues
relating to improvement of the village life - that
the task of development simply got relegated into
the background. In fact this situation did not allow
much development to occur, and where development did
occur it only benefited the powerful and influential
members of the Panchayat or their relatives and
friends. The benefits did not trickle down to the
lowliest in the village.'

The fact is that performance has been very uneven - for
some councils have succeeded to quite a high degree. The
reason may well be that the growth of 'politicalisation,
democratisation and conscientisation' (as *S.C. Varma* puts it)
is necessarily slow, and, it may be added, not helped by
failure in many States to hold the regular elections to
Panchayats and thus give a chance for new leadership to emerge.

One-party organisations, represented at all levels from
village to State, have also appealed to many governments.
They not only give continuous grassroots support to the central
government or head of state, but also supply an element of
initiative at field level and an opportunity to needle the
bureaucracy. The dangers of such organisations are obvious.
They are easily led into technical mistakes, as party policy
rigidifies, regardless of local circumstances; and they have
little patience with opposition, with a tendency to become a
powerful local elite. Not all governments have made the effort,
noticeable in Tanzania, to retain a democratic element in the
party by periodic re-election of local and even national

leaders. One-party systems, typical of the immediately post-colonial period when new governments are establishing themselves, are in a critical sense anti-democratic, because of their exclusion of opposition. A further reference to this topic will be made in the conclusions.

Apart from general political philosophy, the creation of a special agency (or agencies) giving almost the same type of assistance to small farmers which the existing agencies are supposed to give to *all* farmers has obvious administrative hazards, in terms of overlaps and ill-will between the special and the general service: it also can cause a considerable waste of personnel. Similarly, if elected councils are given responsibility (eg for co-ordinating development efforts in their area), these are also the responsibility of any effective co-ordination by officials of their own junior staffs - even if these are nominally seconded to the local council. The stress between the Block Development Officer in India who is the executive officer of the Block Panchayat, seconded from the government service, and the officers of the regular (government) services or of the special IRD agency is a case in point. It is possible that, in an experimental stage, governments have not been willing to commit themselves to hard-and-fast definitions of who does what - but this ambiguity will have to be resolved.

GOVERNMENT ORGANISATION AND MANAGEMENT

Special agencies for small farmers and the poor

There are distinct advantages in the special agency,
recruited mainly from existing Ministry of Agriculture
Extension staff. Such an agency is the Small Farmers
Development Agency in India. It directs the attention
of staff directly to the small and even marginal
farmers, who are their sole concern; it directs technical and research attention to what may be their
peculiar constraints and needs; and it can carry
subsidies particularly directed to this section of the
farming community.[1] Its work is concerned with agricultural services. Later, different special programmes
(Integrated Rural Development and Drought-Prone Area
programmes) were created, particularly concerned, at
the level of individual village families, with
raising incomes by various means, including schemes for
artisanal employment, cottage production, utilisation
of house-plots, etc. At the present time the services
are gradually being unified under District Development
Societies.[2] In some countries a whole special
department is set up for 'Integrated Rural Development',
thereby adding considerable confusion with the field
staff of the main line departments.

---

1 Subsidies are apt to encourage some cheating by
   larger farmers, who may declare fragments of their
   holding under different names.
2 These are legally established as registered Societies
   to which central government can direct support.

47

There is only limited comment on the value of special agencies designed to help the poor. *Judith Tendler* writes:

> I have some thoughts, first, on your question about separate ministries, and your concern that they create confusion and rivalry. This has been a subject that has interested me for some time, and I still feel I have no answer because of the following perpetual dilemma: a separate ministry or department for projects 'targeted' on the poor is desirable because you don't internalize the class conflict in the society at large within the agency itself; extension agents,[1] for example, don't have to turn their backs on a previously existing large-farmer clientele in order to serve a poorer, less politically powerful, and less physically comfortable small-farmer clientele. I feel the strongest argument against it, which creates the dilemma, is that an agency which deals only with poor people is likely to be politically weak. I suggest some ways out of the dilemma in the World Bank paper.[2]

Alec McCallum comments with a limited approval of the special agency, but with a *caveat* that it must not lose touch with agricultural research (which has its normal liaison with the Ministry of Agriculture). In fact in India the special agencies (under the Ministry of Rural Reconstruction) are increasingly to be linked with the agriculture staffs at field levels. But in some other countries the separation of staff does cause a problem of rivalry and confusion, both among the staff and among the farmers.

The special agency, as it has operated in India, has certainly achieved one major step forward, simply by *identifying* the poor in the villages. There is plenty of evidence that before the agency existed,

---

1 The agents of the separate agency, not of the Ministry of Agriculture.
2 Forthcoming, but still confidential.

Extension staffs in India and in many countries no doubt
knew of their existence in theory but had not identified
them by name and place in their area. However, there
remains some doubt how far, after identification, any
major proportion of the poor have in fact been actively
helped. At the present moment this doubt hangs over
the performance of many countries which have proclaimed
anti-poverty programmes and established new agencies or
ministries to implement them.

The multiplicity of agencies and co-ordination

In fact, the new and growing emphasis on: 1) more benefits
to the poor; 2) integrated rural development, to include
both social services and the non-agricultural members
of the rural communities; and 3) participatory development, recapitulate the earlier tensions between agricultural and community development bureaucracies, with
an added element. This is a recognition that both the
farming community and the total community in a village
are not single targets but each divided, between large
farmers and small/marginal farmers, and between the rich
and influential and the poor and powerless, respectively.
To involve small/marginal farmers in new agricultural
activities, or to involve other poor members of the
community in new health or handicraft activities, implies
that the job of the agricultural officer as well as the
social service job is not merely technical but also
consultative, catalytic and organisational.

It now seems clear that, to prevent confusion about
who organises what at village level, some far clearer
definition of functions between the Ministry of Agriculture and other (old or new) ministries is urgently
needed; and that 'Integrated Rural Development', valid
as a statement of intent, has been, and still is, a

grave source of confusion as a *definition of administrative responsibility.* It may be that the principal distinction should be between agricultural services (for farmers large and small) and social services (including employ- ment). Such a division should be administratively feasible. On the agricultural side, it would imply that field staff should involve themselves in helping small farmers and in consulting with them to launch partici- patory programmes. On the social side, a distinction of this type might, if government so wished, facilitate the allocation of at least some social services to an elected council, without confusing the agricultural services structure.

The confusion and cries for 'better co-ordination' arise not only from two closely parallel ministries of agriculture and of social development, but from a much wider multiplicity of departments, parastatal boards and authorities, 'special schemes' and the organisational demands of large donors. As regards the broad division between agriculture and social services, *McCallum, Johnston* and *Clark,* and *N.V. Ratnam* all agree in general terms. *Tendler,* on the other hand, puts in a word of caution, pointing out that the Ministry of Agriculture is usually a more powerful agency than the social services department or ministries, and that in consequence, there is a danger that the poor, already neglected, will have a less powerful advocate on the social side.

As regards the wider multiplicity of agencies, which arises from the tendency to add a new organisation for every new problem, *J.M. Leach* speaks forcibly:

> I agree with the general proposition that
> Ministries of Agriculture should be primarily
> responsible for agricultural production,
> including the human and social aspects of
> such matters. But I do not believe that it

is possible or desirable to be tidy in such
matters . . . Boundaries and definitions are
hazy and difficult to draw when it comes to
such matters as co-operatives, social services,
local government, land, employment, the poor,
women, community development . . . I suggest
it is more profitable to concentrate attention
on linkages, information flows and communications.
The difficulty is not so much that all these
agencies exist as that they do not talk to one
another. Too often the magic word 'co-ordination'
is intoned, co-ordinating committees are appointed,
and then the magic somehow does not work,

In my view the causes of such disappointments
are seldom correctly diagnosed and are often
very simple, straight-forward administrative
or management incompetence. No-one has taken
the trouble to establish an effective secretariat,
the nuts and bolts of organising official committee work have been overlooked, adequate
staffing has been neglected. It would be helpful
if the mystique and mumbo-jumbo of 'co-ordination',
'integrated rural development' and 'decentralisation' could be swept away and replaced by
simple network systems, working through existing
structures and sustained by small, hard-working
and efficient secretariats.

On this formidable problem of co-ordination *Judith
Tendler* raises a more controversial point:

I am not worried about the confusion and rivalry
that separate agencies cause. There is a considerable literature in organisational theory
that suggests that organisational redundancy
and competition is wholesome and healthy. I
have seen cases where more conservative,
established and powerful agencies have eventually
copied the programs of newer, poor-oriented
agencies when they saw that the latter were
being successful . . .

Tendler continues by re-emphasising the importance
of having a powerful agency which may enter fields for
which it is not specially designed with more success than
a weak, though specialised, agency.

As to this comment, there are indeed governments
presently at the stage of having a plethora of often

competing agencies - the Philippines and Sri Lanka are
good examples. It could be argued that, with the
passage of time, the most successful will come out on
top and the less successful be absorbed (the latter a
painful process, usually stoutly resisted). There may
be also a case for some competition between, for example,
bureaucratic services and private enterprise (eg in
credit provision or between traders and a marketing
board, eg in West Africa). But competition between
government departments themselves seems to have little
to recommend it and implies a weakness in central
direction of the administration. There may be much to
be said for: 1) at least two clear groupings at the
centre (agricultural-social service) each with a secretariat (*Leach*), and 2) much stronger 'systems management'
of the same groupings at the operational level ('District').
Rau and *Jaiswal* lean towards a system of: 1) a single
team to assess local (village level) needs and potential,
and 2) resulting action to meet these needs by appropriate
departments (agriculture, health, education, employment,
industry, etc) backed by appropriate entrepreneurial
research and management services (eg for cottage industries).
A consultative and participatory style, at the lowest
level of assessment, is equally applicable to social as
it is to agricultural assessment and programmes.

This may seem to be a tiresome concern with the
formalities of government structure and the nomen-
clature of ministries. But in fact, as the development
effort spreads out more widely to cover the multiple
needs of the poor in rural communities, it is vital
(particularly with official staffs) that responsibilities
should be clarified. There will be multiple points of
contact and ways of organising groups, for farming, for
irrigation management, for health, nutrition, family
planning, for developing artisanal or home-production

skills, most of which will involve some form of official
support or guidance. It is important the channels for
support should be clear.

The complexity of organisation cannot be wished
away. Certainly, a small reduction in the number of
agencies might be achieved if old agencies were reformed
instead of adding new ones; but that is not enough.
Taking into account the foregoing comments, it may be
that a major improvement could be achieved 1) at the
centre, forming distinct clusters of ministries, each
served by a secretariat. These clusters might be a)
agriculture, b) social services, c) employment services.
They would be concerned with policy. 2) The same
clusters at the (District) operational level, under a
single management with clear authority to co-ordinate
all operational decisions; and similar clusters at sub-
District level, with considerable financial flexibility.
3) At the field level, a small team for consultation or
'diagnosis' and preliminary programming for helping to
organise small functional groups, and for calling down
expert help from the wide variety of expertise and
services above them.

*Policy control and operational control: delegation and
co-ordination*

This is inevitably a confused scene, with many variations
in ministries and other agencies between different
governments. But it is possible to isolate a few main
issues which are common to at least the majority of
governments which are seriously interested in reaching
small farmers and, in some cases, a wider range of the
rural poor.

First, there must be concern for coherent *policy
making*; and it is suggested (above) that this would be

helped by some grouping of departments concerned with
agricultural development, of other departments concerned
with social services, and possibly a third group concerned with rural industries, artisans, employment
policy; each group to be served by an adequate secretariat.

Second, there must be concern with flexibility in
operations, if the needs and wishes of farmers in very
varied local circumstances are to be taken into account.
Thus flexibility has to come from an operational command
much lower down the hierarchy, a point which may be
arbitrarily called 'the District'. Whatever it is
called, it must be a point where there is a level of
staffing, both administrative and technical, adequate
to manage and co-ordinate programmes running in the
District which involve many departments and agencies.
This must involve considerable delegation of finance
and authority from the policy-making centre, with
certain nationally decided limits. This will only be
achieved if a strict distinction is made between policy-
making and local operations.

Many governments have, in fact, recognised the need
for such a managing and co-ordinating centre at District
level; and in many cases a senior administrator (whom
we will call a District Commissioner[1] or a District
Minister) has been appointed as the leader and co-
ordinator of operations. But in fact this officer has
almost never been given the authority or the financial
resources needed to do the job. This is partly due to
the mistrust of Treasury; but it is perhaps even more
due to the doctrine of   departmental sovereignty, by
which each department claims complete control over its

---

1   There are, of course, many other titled - Collector,
    District Magistrate, Government Agent, Chief District
    Officer, etc.

own staff, right down to their lowest position. The
formula that District Departmental Officers are technically responsible to their department, but operationally
responsible to the District Commissioner has never
worked well, not least because the pay, promotion and
prospects of the officer depend upon his department at
the centre, not on the District administrator. Thus
delegation and co-ordination are inextricably linked;
for the District management cannot manage a team in
which individuals are getting conflicting instructions
from on high. There is a case here, if anywhere, for
'systems management', because multiple agencies are
involved. But neither the structure nor the authority
has been available. Matters have been made worse by
the increasing complexity of development administration,
with a constant increase in departments and parastatals,
and a consequent gross overloading of the District
Commissioner's post and (ironically) in some countries
a down-grading of his status, though without a substitute
method of co-ordination.

The particular relevance of these general issues to
the service of small farmers is most clearly illustrated
from the planning and programming function. Obviously,
some things must be initially planned at the centre - a
large irrigation scheme covering several Districts, or
the financial allocations between departments; some
rather smaller schemes at the District level. But if any
serious attempt to consult farmers or assist them to
manage their own schemes is to be made, then the village-
level programmes must be planned, after diagnosis, at
local level; and presumably these will come up to sub-
District for aggregation, and next, to District. The
District is then faced with a double task of aggregating
and reconciling these up-coming schemes and fitting them
into certain major schemes coming down to District from

the centre. The management of this task demands, in
the last resort, a recognisable management structure
which would probably resemble more closely the top
management of a parastatal board (with the necessary
functional divisions) than the array of departmental
District Officers, each of semi-sovereign authority.
It is hard to find any other method which avoids top-
down and ill-co-ordinated programmes, largely devised
by the central government, being imposed finally at
the farmers' and villagers' level. Moreover, even the
big projects, rightly planned in outline from the
centre, have to be executed at very local levels. It
is encouraging that even in a large surface irrigation
scheme, which exists solely to bring water to the
farmers' fields, water allocation can be managed at
field level by small water-users' groups. *David Korten*
suggests (by letter) that, instead of a head-on attack
on the whole bureaucratic system, retraining and re-
organisation might well be tackled function by function
(irrigation, forestry, pastoral management, etc),
ending in each case with a strong local management
contribution.

Whatever the detailed application, there will
always be the need, outlined above, for a strong District
management unit. In countries which are committed
strongly to local democratic councils, these can still
be fitted into the operational system (as, for example,
in Maharashtra, where the elected District Council -
(Zila Parishad) virtually manages agricultural development
through its own committees and its own senior executive
and staff).

PART IV: CONCLUSIONS

CONCLUSIONS

Few, if any, governments of developing countries would
deny that it is socially desirable to include a major
larger section of their rural population - the poorer
section - in development output and benefits. Perhaps
rather more would plead that their resources are inadequate
at present to take on extra expenditure in such an effort,
even if in the medium-term at least both economic and
socio-political gains would result; and in some, the
suspicion that more investment in the poor would mean less
gain to the rich may result in political opposition. This
Occasional Paper has endeavoured to set out in some detail
just what changes in direction and administration would be
necessary for any government which, despite these hesitations,
is nevertheless determined to attempt a programme much
more deliberately directed towards small and marginal
farmers and farm labourers.

Its major conclusion is that such an attempt cannot
be confined to some single special agency, or indeed to
any one part of the existing agricultural development
administration. It is not a question *only* of retraining
the agricultural field services; or of altering the
content of research and of technological programmes; or
of more investment in the systems of delivering inputs;
or of tenancy reform. Each of these is important in itself.
The argument here is that agricultural development is a
system in which all these factors are facets, and that to
adapt it to a new constituency with special needs and

constraints involves complementary changes in many parts
of the system, including changes in attitudes and style
of action as well as structural and functional changes.

Perhaps the allegation that governments lack the
political will to make such changes have been over-emphasised;
there are many which have demonstrated - often by establishing
new departments or institutions - that the will is not
lacking. It is suggested here that in many such cases it
is not lack of will but four other factors which have
hindered success. The first is an incautious choice of
institutional methods of implementation, leaving open far
too many opportunities for the power structure in the rural
areas to capture benefits intended for the poor. The second
is a concentration, in aid of quick economic gains, on the
areas of highest potential and on the farmers best equipped,
in resources and sophistication, to adopt sophisticated
(and capital-intensive) programmes. The third, and not the
least difficult to overcome, lies in the rigidity and
conservatism of the administrative (bureaucratic) system,
highly centralised and sharply compartmented in powerful
departments. The fourth is quite simply managerial failure
to make an admittedly complex system work.

It has been constantly emphasised that small-holding
agriculture is highly locale-specific, both technically
and socially. It would certainly seem strange to apply
to such a system such a highly centralised bureaucratic
system. This will explain the emphasis in this Occasional
Paper on local assessment of potential; on local, consultative building of programmes; on a single, less compartmented
operational management at the 'District' level; on a very
careful choice of what institutions to support at local
levels, having regard to the power structure; and on

variations in the technology and programme content, backed
by research, for those farmers for whom the minimising of
both financial and technical work is of overriding
importance.

In terms of administration, the inevitable complexity
of agencies dealing with so many aspects of agricultural
development (contact, supplies, tools, credit, storage,
marketing, access, power, irrigation, crops and animals)
has been further increased by the loose attachment of
'integrated rural development' programmes concerned with
social services to the poor (whether on farms or not) and
employment income-raising programmes which may have some
agricultural content (eg dairy) or a semi-industrial content
(cottage industry, artisans, small processing ventures,
etc), making it difficult to keep a clear distinction
between agricultural and social service or employment
programmes. Co-ordination over such a variety of activities
is almost impossible and very time-consuming. The emphasis
here has been a rough grouping of types of activity, so that
the span of interests is reduced in each of two or more
groupings. The agricultural grouping is by far the most
in need of constant co-ordination of services because of
the rigid time constraints (sowing, fertilising, irrigating)
and the variations in weather conditions; social services
can afford a more leisurely gait, with less danger of
'capture'.

In terms of planning, the upward movement of programme
design from the farm level is obviously of key importance;
and this implies a planning contribution from each ascending
level - sub-District, District, centre - involving not only
plan content, but the corresponding personnel, supply and
financial aspects.

There is nothing inherently impossible in these
multiple modifications in the systems concerned; nor in
the cost of such changes, mainly in retraining and some
redistribution of existing staff. But the change in
perception of their role, by field and intermediate staff,
from concepts of delivering packages of information, advice,
down a hierarchy of superiors and inferiors, to a consultative
approach concerned with building up the capacity and
initiative of farmers, may well prove very difficult.
Similarly, at a higher level, any whole-hearted approach
to delegation of authority and finance is bound to meet with
grave obstacles and reluctance from each layer of the
bureaucracy.

The question of what degree of authority and finance
should be given to elected councils at District level and
below (including village councils) is one which depends on
the circumstances and the philosophy of different countries
and on the time-scale which may be set for such democratisation. Clearly, in some countries which have only
a single generation of independent political experience,
or which have strong regional differences, or are desperately
short of trained personnel in the rural economy, delegation
of power will not come easily. It would certainly seem that
democracy is most real at its lowest, face-to-face level of
the village or group of villages; and that, at higher
levels, administrative and economic issues (and political
ambitions) may predominate over direct concern with the
village poor. But the speed and methods by which democratic
organisation can be nurtured at each level, from village
upwards, is a matter which each country will settle
differently. It is fairly easy to devolve social and
municipal services; but the devolution of agricultural
development responsibility, with all its complex, interlocked activities, and with its varied requirements of
expertise, is a much more adventurous proposition.

Finally this statement of 'requirements' cannot be a suggestion for early total implementation. It is the signpost for a direction of advance. There are many but very localised signs of technical consultation at very local levels; there are signs of more local planning. Here and there are signs of more truly adaptive and farm management research. Altering the structure and attitudinal change in the bureaucracy and resolving overlaps between Extension (and other offical services) and community development and elected councils will take much longer to grow. In the longer term it is certainly desirable that such bodies should take over much of the work now attempted by a growing number of separate official services at local level. Each change in a single direction will imply and perhaps stimulate comple-mentary changes. Experience (eg with small groups) will give better evidence and, no doubt, amendment to the suggestions outlined here. Perhaps this outline of the range of tasks, so closely interlocked, will be helpful at this stage.

APPENDIX

Commentators

R. N. Azad	Commonwealth Secretariat, London.
N. S. Carey Jones	Colonial Service (RTD).
* R. Chambers	Ford Foundation, New Delhi.
T. N. Chatmvedi	Secretary (Government of India), Ministry of Home Affairs, New Delhi.
* G. Etienne	Ecole Superieur des Hautes Etudes, Geneva.
G. Hyden	Ford Foundation, Nairobi.
J. Jacobs	Colonial Administration and Institute of Development Studies, University of Sussex (RTD)
J. Jiggins	International Agricultural Centre, Wageningen, Netherlands.
* B. F. Johnston and W. C. Clarke	(Forthcoming publication) Food Research Institute, Stanford University, California.
R. King	University of Reading, Department of Agricultural Economics.
* D. C. Korten	Asian Institute of Management, Manila.
J. W. Leach	Consultant for Overseas Development Administration, London.
H. M. Mathur	Joint Secretary (Government of India), Ministry of Home Affairs, New Delhi.
A. McCallum	FAO (Institutions Service), Rome.
* A. Z. Obaidullah Khan	Secretary, Ministry of Agriculture, Bangladesh.
N. V. Ratnam	Indian Institute of Management, Bangalore.
S. K. Rau and N. K. Jaiswal	National Institute of Rural Development, Hyderabad, India.

* Not comments, but recent publications mentioned.

Neils Röling	International Agricultural Centre, Wageningen, Netherlands.
* J. G. Ryan	ICRISAT, Hyderabad, India.
R. J. G. Steele	Ministry of Agriculture, Lesotho.
* J. Tendler	Consultant, Berkeley, California.
N. T. Uphoff	Cornell University, Ithaca, New York.
* S. C. Varma	Secretary (Government of India), Ministry of Home Affairs, New Delhi.